A boy called Robbie

A boy called Robbie

A Popjustice Book
Illustrated by David Whittle

First published in Great Britain in 2006 by Friday Books
An imprint of The Friday Project Limited
83 Victoria Street, London SW1H 0HW

www.thefridayproject.co.uk
www.fridaybooks.co.uk

Text © Peter Robinson 2006
Illustrations © David Whittle 2006

ISBN – 10   0 9548318 5 3
ISBN – 13   978 0 9548318 5 1

British Library Cataloguing in Publication Data

A catalogue record for this book is available
from the British Library

Designed and produced by Staziker Jones
www.stazikerjones.co.uk

The Publisher's policy is to use paper
manufactured from sustainable sources

This book belongs to

_____

I am ____ years old

My favourite Robbie song is ——————

When I grow up, I want to be ——————

Here is my autograph!

_____

This is Robbie.

Robbie likes to sing songs.

Unfortunately, sometimes singing songs makes Robbie all sad.

Robbie gets sad because people like him and he is very rich with a nice house.

What a silly billy!

One day a very long time ago Robbie made four friends.

Howard was handsome and strong.

Jason was handsome and smiled a lot.

Mark was handsome and girls wanted to cuddle him.

Gary wrote songs.

Some people thought that Robbie and his friends liked to kiss each other.

Even though they did not do any kissing, Robbie and his friends never said that they did kiss or that they didn't kiss.

It seemed like a mystery – and this made people interested!

Robbie, Howard, Jason and Mark, and Gary, formed a band together.

They called the band Take That. It was a silly name, but after a while people forgot that it was silly because they liked the band so much.

They sang lots of songs together, and became very famous all around the world.

But not in America.

One summer, Robbie made some new friends. Their names were Noel and Liam and Robbie went with them to a big pop concert in the countryside.

He had fun at the concert. He ate sweets and drank fizzy pop. As you can imagine, all the sugar went right to Robbie's head!

Robbie jumped up and down all night, and didn't go to bed until very late!

Unfortunately, Gary, Jason, Howard and Mark did not like Robbie's new friends. They said Robbie's new friends were a bad influence!

They were very upset that Robbie had gone to the countryside without them.

In fact they were so upset that they said Robbie was no longer welcome in Take That!

Without his friends, Robbie was very upset.

He ate lots of cakes to make himself happy.

To make matters worse, Robbie's new friends Noel and Liam decided they did not like him either!

They called him a 'fat dancer'. That was unfair – Robbie could sing as well!

Noel and Liam's bullying upset Robbie, because everyone listened to what they said.

Except in America.

Robbie was very good at singing songs, but he was not very good yet at making them up.

He met a man called Guy. Guy could make up songs but was not very good at singing them.

One very special day, Guy made up a song called 'Angels', and Robbie sang along to it.

'Angels' was a slow song.

It made many people cry because it was so sad. But everyone liked it.

They liked it so much that Robbie became very very famous.

But not in America.

Sometimes Robbie liked to put lots of clothes on.

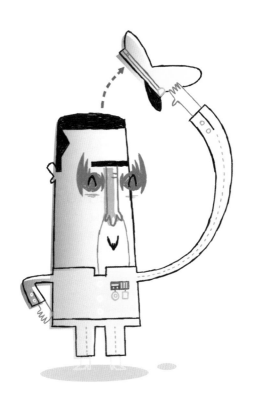

Sometimes Robbie liked to take everything off.

One day Robbie became very sad because he stopped being friends with Guy.

But there was a happy ending because Guy made some new friends.

Robbie made a new friend too. The new friend's name was Stephen. Just like Guy, Stephen could make up very good songs.

In 2005, a boy called Bob held a big concert in London.

But the concert was not for fun. It was to save the world.

'Will you help save the world?' asked Bob.

'I would love to!' said Robbie.

Robbie stole the show!

And that is how a boy called Robbie became the very best singer in the world.

Sometimes he is still sad about being rich and famous, but he knows there is always one place he can go and not be recognised.

America!

Here are Robbie and his pal Gary.
Sometimes they are nice to each other and
sometimes they are mean to each other.

You can cut out Robbie and Gary (ask an
adult to do the difficult bits!), stick them to
your fingers and act out scenes.

Robbie: Ooh Gary you are rubbish!
Gary: No I am not!
Robbie: I am better than you!
Gary: No you are not!

Hours of fun!

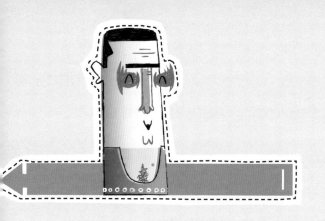

Popjustice.com is the greatest pop website on the face of Planet Earth. We update every day with the best pop stuff.

Drop in at **www.popjustice.com/idols** for downloadable wallpapers, screensavers and other random nonsense.

Why not send us an email? idols@popjustice.com